Fairy Tales

 pi kids® publications international, ltd.

The Prince must find the young lady whose foot fits the little glass slipper he found. Can you help the Prince find Cinderella? Look for the fellows below, too. Help them find their true loves. Their darling damsels are also missing one shoe!

Cinderella

Frank N. Stein

Long John Silver

Joe Bowler

Surfer Doodz

Rex Rodeo

Bob E. Soxer

I. C. Skater

When the Three Little Pigs grew up, they started Bacon Brothers Construction Company. They built lots of famous buildings! Can you find the Three Little Pigs? Do you see the Big Bad Wolf? Have fun looking for these buildings, too!

Francis Bacon

Quisp Bacon

Fats Bacon

The Eye-ful Tower

Big Bad Wolf

The Ears Tower

The Leaning Tower of Pizza

Banished to the woods for being so beautiful, Snow White took refuge at the Seven Dwarfs Hotel. The Wicked Queen is still looking for Snow White, though. Find the Seven Dwarfs so they can warn Snow White about the Queen. Then try to find Snow White, too!

Snow White

Fuss

Blip

Glitch

Byte

Bonsai

Bit

Fidget

7 Dwarfs Hotel

Baby Contest

SHRIMP COCKTAIL LOUNGE

Jockey Convention

Valet Parking

Little Red Riding Hood is going to visit her granny on the other side of the forest. Her path is full of danger! There are many Big Bad Wolves who would like to have Little Red for supper! First find Little Red and her granny. Then look for these dangers throughout the forest.

Little Red

Granny

A wolf with a slingshot

A wolf with dynamite

A wolf with a net

A wolf with a sack

A wolf in disguise

A wolf with a rope

There's been a break-in. Some porridge is missing, a chair is broken, and beds are slept in. We have an idea "whodunit." A kid named Goldilocks has been seen in the area. We know one thing for sure: she has bad manners. Will you help find these characters and clues at the scene of the crime?

Goldilocks

Papa Bear

Mama Bear

Baby Bear

Lt. Clod-dumbo

Detective Sure-Lock Holmes

A broken chair

Goldilocks' ribbon

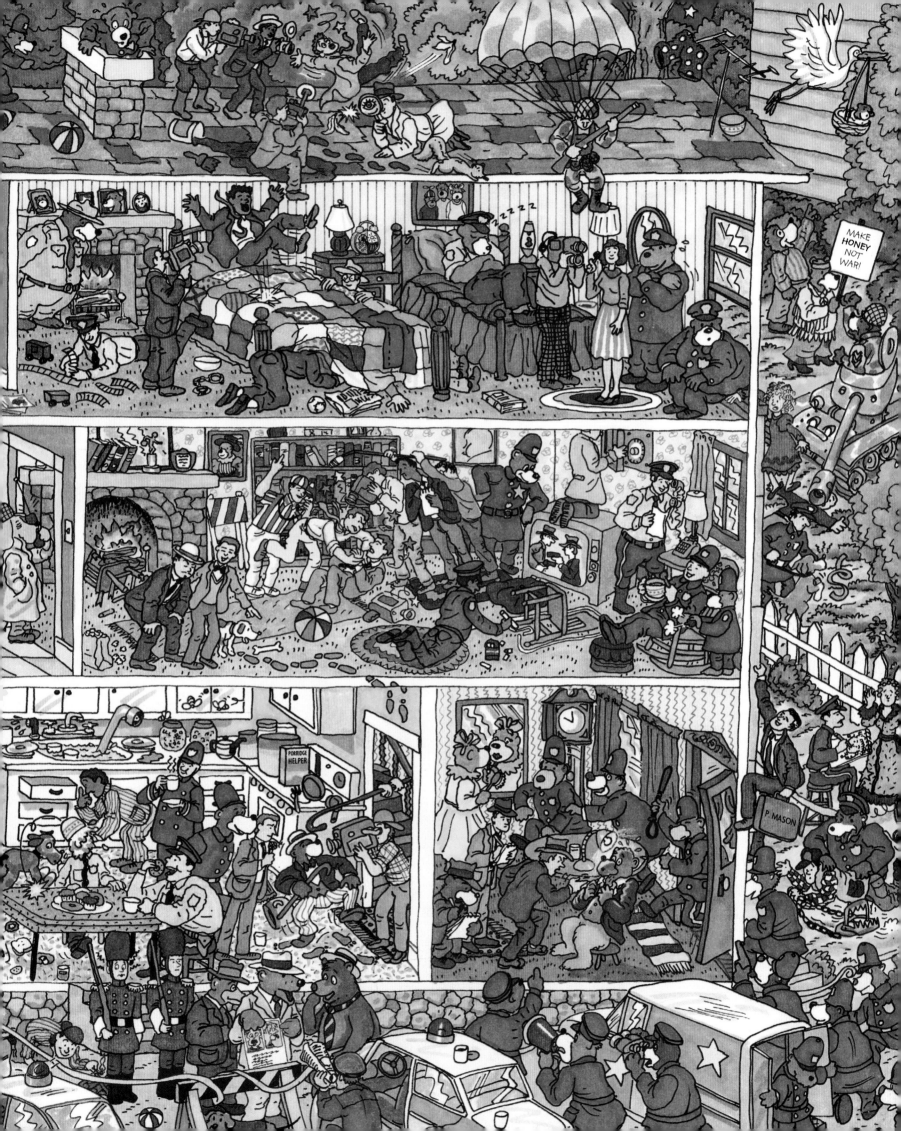

Life in Neptune's kingdom went swimmingly until the Little Mermaid saved the Prince's life. She has fallen head over fins in love – and even wishes she were human! First, find the Little Mermaid. Next, look for these human things that mermaids cannot use.

The Little Mermaid

A pair of pants

A bicycle

Panty hose

Sneakers

Roller skates

Socks

A pogo stick

Once the wicked witch was gone, Hansel and Gretel started eating up the gingerbread house. But there were so many goodies, they invited all their friends to join in the fun! After you find Hansel and Gretel, look for these *sweet* kids!

Hansel

Gretel

Cinnamon-Swirl Pearl

Cotton-Candy Andy

Lolly Pop

Gingerbread Fred

Bubbles Gumm

Chip Chocolate

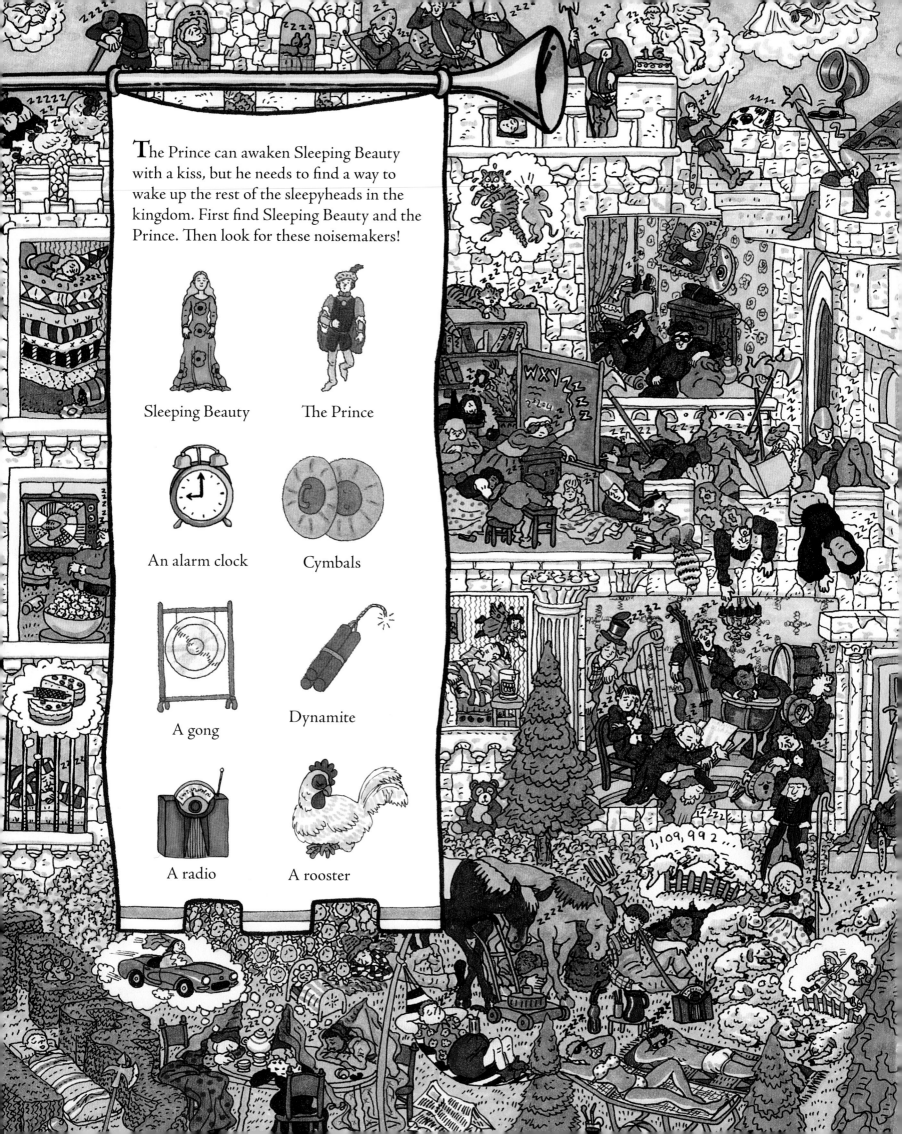

The Prince can awaken Sleeping Beauty with a kiss, but he needs to find a way to wake up the rest of the sleepyheads in the kingdom. First find Sleeping Beauty and the Prince. Then look for these noisemakers!

Sleeping Beauty

The Prince

An alarm clock

Cymbals

A gong

Dynamite

A radio

A rooster

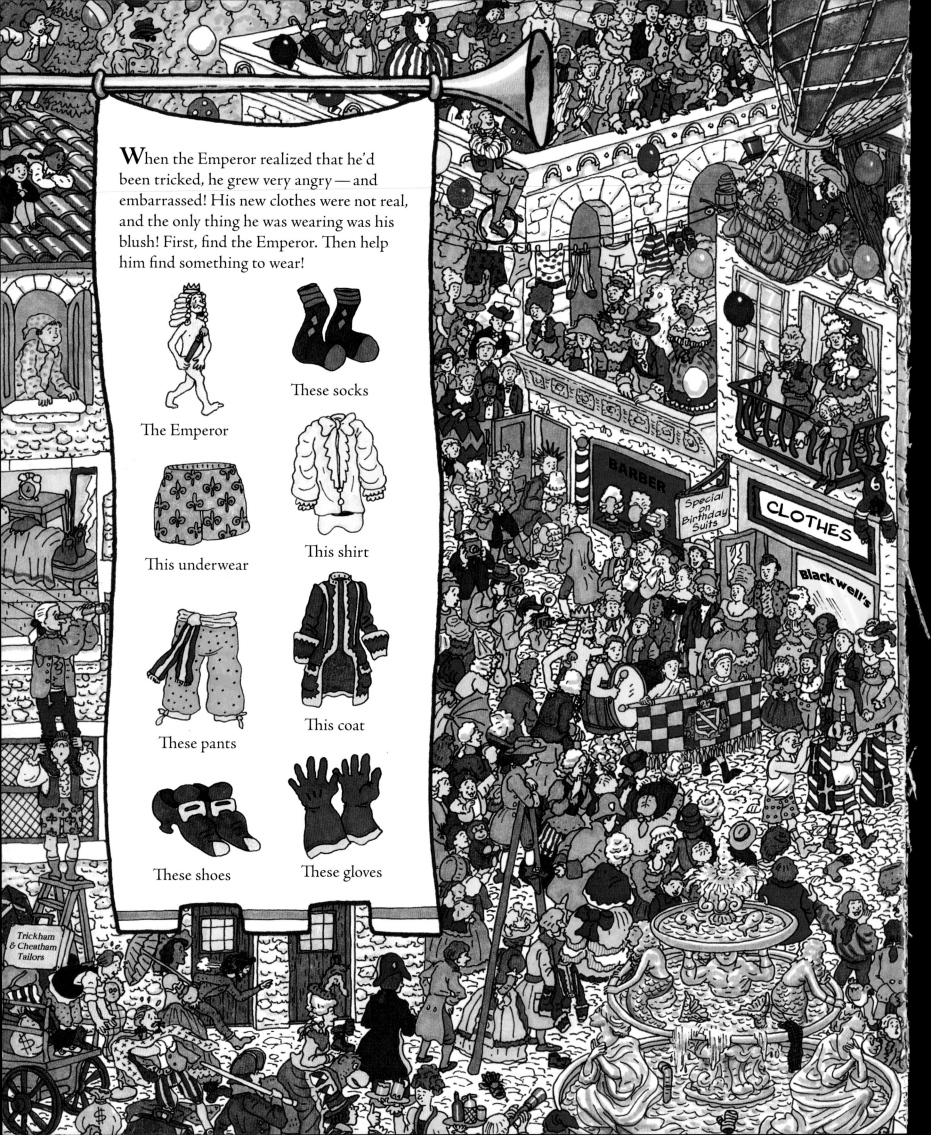

When the Emperor realized that he'd been tricked, he grew very angry — and embarrassed! His new clothes were not real, and the only thing he was wearing was his blush! First, find the Emperor. Then help him find something to wear!

The Emperor

These socks

This underwear

This shirt

These pants

This coat

These shoes

These gloves

Trickham & Cheatham Tailors

BARBER

Special on Birthday Suits

CLOTHES

Blackwell's

The glass slipper wasn't the only shoe that was lost in the Cinderella story. Can you find these other missing shoes?

A ballet slipper
A snowshoe
A roller skate
A scuba flipper
A baby bootie
An alligator shoe

Take another trip to Pig City. Do you see these different kinds of houses?

An igloo
A sand castle
A tree house
An adobe house
A pagoda
A haunted house
A tepee
A birdhouse

Go back to the Seven Dwarfs Hotel. Can you find these other sevens?

777 Seventh Avenue
Seven birthday candles
Seven swans a-swimming
Lucky sevens
Seven brides
Septuplets
Chapter 7

Little Red's goodies spilled out of her basket. Can you find them?

A birthday cake
A bottle of milk
A wedge of cheese
A string of sausage
A loaf of bread
A bouquet of flowers
A box of chocolates
A can of WOLF OFF spray

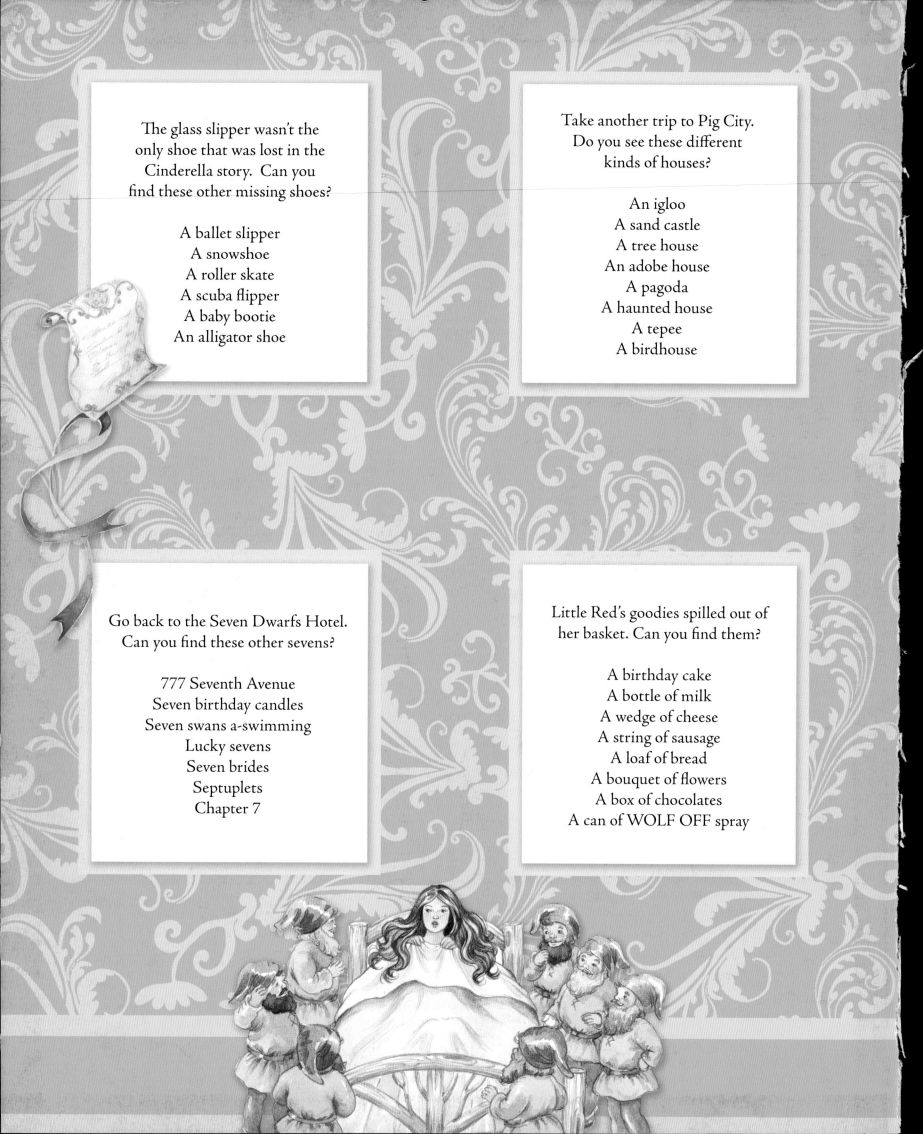